best friends
always...

...giggle when
you're silly

bang on the door ™ ©

best friends

Collins

First published in Great Britain
by HarperCollins Publishers Ltd in 2003

1 3 5 7 9 10 8 6 4 2

ISBN: 0-00-715205-1

Bang on the door character copyright:
© 2003 Bang on the Door all rights reserved.
bang on the door is a trademark
Exclusive right to license by Santoro

www.bangonthedoor.com

Text © 2003 HarperCollins Publishers Ltd

A CIP catalogue record for this title is available from the British Library.

Printed in Hong Kong
Bound in China

...have fun in
all weathers

...help when you
need them

...lend you
their clothes

...make you
special presents

...trust you
with their
secrets

...tell you when you're a fashion disaster

...stick together!